THE FAIR OF FLAR

Clive Gifford

Roller Ghoster!

Trolley of Terror!

Illustrated by Jacqueline East

Terri and Clare were going
to a brand new fair.
It had appeared yesterday,
almost out of thin air.

Clare was excited and chose to wear
trainers with her flares.
Terri brushed her hair.
She was more than a little scared.
Who wouldn't be scared, going to a
place called the **Fair of Fear**?

The pair rode their scooters
to the fair on the square.
"There's nobody here –
we're the first ones!" cheered Clare.
"Come on, Terri, you like to share scares."

"Yeah, you find something that makes me scared," Terri dared.
The fair was eerie, but she acted as if she didn't care.

2

These words have the letters **ear** in them, but not all of them rhyme with the word **ear**. Circle those words that do.

spear

bear

gear

swear

wear

pear

clear

appear

The Fair of Fear was set out
on a place called Scare Square.
Even with fairy lights,
the fair looked dreary and eerie.
Ghoul Tour was shut
and Werewolf World was not open until next year.
Even the Roller Ghoster was closed to undergo repair.
The sign said this was due to much wear and tear.

Mare of Despair

Ghoul To...   SHUT

"Look over there!" shouted Terri.
"There's a ride called the Mare of Despair!"
But it was just a silly rocking horse with spiky hair.

"That's barely scary at all," said Terri. Clare just glared.
She was getting angry, as there was nothing to fear.

4

The words **fare** and **fair** sound the same, but are spelt differently. Can you choose and write out the correct word for each of these sentences?

1. Terri brushed her **hair hare** _____ .

2. Clare chose to **wear where** _____ her trainers.

3. Behind them, the scampi **through threw** _____ more spears.

4. Terri tried to **peer pier** _____ over the screen.

5. Blair Fear stared down at the **pear pair** _____ of girls.

6. The **stairs stares** _____ led up to the Bear's Lair.

7. Terri and Clare **road rode** _____ their scooters to the fair.

8. "Spear, scar and snare them – pull out **there their** _____ hair!"

5

Terri and Clare paid the fare to see the rare bearded lady. "Be prepared to be very scared," read the sign.

"Let's be careful, Clare," warned Terri.

The pair **peered** over a screen and followed the trail of hair. It was a long flowing beard, but attached to a man.

"The bearded lady is ill,
so I am taking her place," he sneered.

"A bearded **man** is not rare," jeered Clare!
"It's a trick, it's not fair."

Terri took Clare to
Mary's Scary Dairy to cheer her up.
The menu looked fun, and Terri
chose the pear ice scream.

6

Which of these words can have an S added to their start to make a new word?

club

coop

care

hare

cute

head

crew

cone

chew

"Ice scream is off and so are scary scones," said Mary.

"Is there anything to eat here?" asked Clare.

Mary gave them a plate and two wooden sticks.
"Here's my killer scampi, cooked rare, with tar-terror sauce."

"Tar-terror sauce?" asked Terri, wide-eyed with **fear**.

"Well, tartar sauce, but tar-terror sounds scarier," said Mary.
The pair shared the scampi using their sticks as tiny spears.

tar-terror sauce

"Spare me, Terri, don't spear me," said Terri in a funny voice.
Clare giggled, speared a scampi and dabbed it in the dip.
"Try the Bear's Lair next." This was Mary's tip.

Say the word **air** and listen to the sound it makes. Now read these sentences and circle any words that have the **air** sound in them.

1. Terri and Clare were going to a brand new fair.

2. The pair rode their scooters to the fair on the square.

Mare of Despair

3. The sign said this was due to much wear and tear.

4. "There's a ride called the Mare of Despair!"

5. "Are you aware we have a vampire bear here?"

6. "So, you care for a dare?" said a man with fair hair.

7. "Clare, Clare!" Terri screamed. "Look over there!"

8. "There, there, my dears," said Blair Fear, staring down at the pair.

"Beware the Bear's Lair," cried a man with one ear.
"Climb the stairs to stare at the scariest of bears!"
Terri thought that two pounds to see a bear was dear.

"Are you aware we have
a Vampire bear here?"

"That's how I lost my ear,"
the man explained.

Clare paid for them both,
and the pair climbed the stairs.
But the scary bear was just a
teddy bear with fake vampire teeth.
Clare despaired, and declared this fair
the worst anywhere.

10

"There is nothing to fear here.
I dare this fair to **scare** me!"

Complete each sentence by writing **before** or **after** in the gap.

1. Terri rode her scooter _____ she had brushed her hair.

2. The two girls arrived at the fair _____ any other visitors.

3. The girls ate scampi _____ they visited the Mare of Despair ride.

4. The girls ordered food _____ they visited the Bear's Lair.

5. They paid the fare _____ climbing the stairs.

6. The pair ordered scampi _____ Mary told them ice scream was off.

7. The girls spotted three closed rides _____ finding one that was open.

8. Terri took Clare to Mary's Scary Dairy _____ they saw the bearded man.

"So, you care for a dare?"
said a man with fair hair.
Terri and Clare jumped, as he
had appeared from nowhere.

"My name is Blair Fear
and this is my fair.
Care to go on my latest ride?
It will give you a nightmare."

Trolley of Terror

"What, like the Teddy Bear's Lair,
or the bearded man?" scoffed Clare.

She was still upset at not being scared.

"Now, now, my dear," said Blair Fear, "I have a flair for fear.
The Trolley of Terror will give you plenty of scares, I swear."

Blair Fear showed the girls inside a tent, which was nearly bare.
Nothing but an old shopping trolley was there.

Synonyms are words that have a similar meaning to each other. Which of these words are synonyms of scared?

tired   fearful   cheerful   bored   horrified   annoyed

frightened   peaceful   bashful   terrified   depressed   calm

shocked   delighted   petrified   frustrated   afraid

The shopping trolley had two chairs and Clare and Terri climbed in.

"Pah," snorted Clare, "I despair of Blair Fear and his fair."
"Clare, can't you hear? There's something near," said Terri.

A scraping sound filled the air.
Slowly, the trolley started moving down a track.

"Yippeee!" cried Clare, as the trolley took them past a torture rack.
Then on past ghosts and fearsome monsters, which bared their teeth.

One ghost cried, "I will tear you girls apart, you creeps!"

"Wow, this is scary," said Clare. "Cool!"
Terri, though, was white with fear as she looked to the rear.

14

Each of these words has another word hidden inside. Use the clues to help you find the hidden words.

scare   a type of transport   _____

flowing   not tall or high up   _____

giant   a type of insect   _____

spears   a type of fruit   _____

scampi   to live in a tent   _____

bearded   a large, furry animal   _____

despaired   two of something   _____

fraction   what actors do   _____

brakes   a garden tool   _____

forget   to fake something   _____

"Remember, Clare, how we speared scampi for lunch? Their bigger brothers and sisters are now after us to munch!"

Clare looked to the rear.
Now she was full of fear.
Giant scampi, as tall as bears,
were chasing and getting near.
They were armed with large wooden spears.

"Yikes!" Clare cried, as a spear flew past her ear.
Terri trembled as another spear flew past her.
Its tip missed her with a fraction to spare.

The scampi cried, "Spear, scar and snare them
– pull out their hair!"
The girls wished they hadn't agreed to Blair Fear's dare.

16

Find the correct answer to each of these scary joke questions and write it in the space.

1. What fairy story includes a ghost? _____

2. What trees do dead monsters like best? _____

3. What is a witch's favourite subject in school? _____

4. What do witches wear on their hair? _____

5. How do ghouls like their eggs? _____

6. What is a ghost's favourite soup? _____

Scream of tomato!

Scare- spray!

Spelling!

Terri-fried!

Ceme-trees!

Ghoul-Deluxe and the three bears!

Clare said her prayers. She was so, so scared.
Hot tears smeared her face, as the spears flew round her ears.

"Clare, Clare!" Terri screamed. "Look over there!"
The pair looked at the track ahead. It ended in mid-air.

"The trolley has no brakes
or steering gear," cried Clare.

Clare trembled like **jelly**
as they got near to the end of the track.
Behind them, the scampi threw more spears.

Then the trolley reached the end and
fell
through
the
air.

Clare and Terri closed their eyes and screamed.
This was their worst **ever** nightmare!

18

Write a short scary scene using these words and phrases to help you.

a moaning sound   black   terrified   as cold as ice

tall as a tree   trembled   screamed

The clock struck midnight and I was alone at home.

_____

_____

_____

_____

_____

19

When they opened their eyes, the girls were back in Scare Square. The Trolley of Terror had vanished into thin air.

"There, there, my dears," said Blair Fear, staring down at the pair. "Did the trolley, ghosts and scampi cause you despair?"

"It was so scary, Mr Fear," said Terri. "A real nightmare."

"Well, I do have a flair for scares, and you wanted a dare," he replied.

"Care for another trip down the tracks?" he asked.

"No Fear!" screamed the pair, who'd had more than their fair share. They leapt onto their scooters and raced away from Scare Square. It would take many years to forget the **Fair of Fear**!

Answer these questions about the story of Terri and Clare, and their visit to the Fair of Fear.

1. What sort of shoes did Clare wear to the fair? _____

2. Which ride at the Fair of Fear was under repair? _____

3. What food did Mary say was off the menu? _____

4. What was the name of the sauce that came with the killer scampi? _____

5. How much did it cost to see the Bear's Lair? _____

6. Which of the girls spotted the giant scampi first? _____

7. What was the name of the man who owned the fair? _____

8. What was the name of the last ride that the girls went on? _____

21

Answers

Page 3

circled words: spear, gear, clear, appear

Page 5

1. hair
2. wear
3. threw
4. peer
5. pair
6. stairs
7. rode
8. their

Page 7

coop ➔ scoop

care ➔ scare

hare ➔ share

crew ➔ screw

cone ➔ scone

Page 9

1. Terri and (Clare) were going to a brand new (fair).
2. The (pair) rode (their) scooters to the (fair) on the (square).
3. The sign said this was due to much (wear) and (tear).
4. "(There's) a ride called the (Mare) of (Despair)!"
5. "Are you (aware) we have a vampire (bear) here?"
6. "So, you (care) for a (dare)?" said a man with (fair) (hair).
7. "(Clare), (Clare)!" Terri screamed. "Look over (there)!"
8. "(There), (there), my dears," said (Blair) Fear, (staring) down at the (pair).

Page 11

1. after	5. before
2. before	6. after
3. after	7. before
4. before	8. after

Page 13

synonyms of scared:
fearful, horrified, frightened, terrified, shocked, petrified, afraid.

Page 15

scare ➔ car

flowing ➔ low

giant ➔ ant

spears ➔ pear

scampi ➔ camp

bearded ➔ bear

despaired ➔ pair

fraction ➔ act

brakes ➔ rake

forget ➔ forge

Page 17

1. Ghoul-Deluxe and the three bears!

2. Ceme-trees!

3. Spelling!

4. Scare-spray!

5. Terri-fried!

6. Scream of tomato!

Page 19

Check your child has used the words and phrases provided.

Page 21

1. trainers

2. the Roller Ghoster

3. ice scream and scary scones

4. tar-terror sauce

5. two pound

6. Terri

7. Blair Fear

8. the Trolley of Terror

Published 2004

Letts Educational, The Chiswick Centre,
414 Chiswick High Road, London W4 5TF
Tel 020 8996 3333   Fax 020 8996 8390
Email mail@lettsed.co.uk
www.letts-education.com

Text, design and illustrations © Letts Educational Ltd 2004

Book Concept, Development and Series Editor:
Helen Jacobs, Publishing Director
Author: Clive Gifford
Book Design: 2idesign Ltd, Cambridge
Illustrations: Jacqueline East, The Bright Agency

Letts Educational Limited is a division of Granada Learning.
Part of Granada plc.
British Library Cataloguing in Publication Data

A CIP record for this book is available from the British Library.

ISBN 1 84315 454 4

Printed in Italy

Colour reproduction by PDQ Digital Media Solutions Ltd, Bungay,
Suffolk NR35 1BY